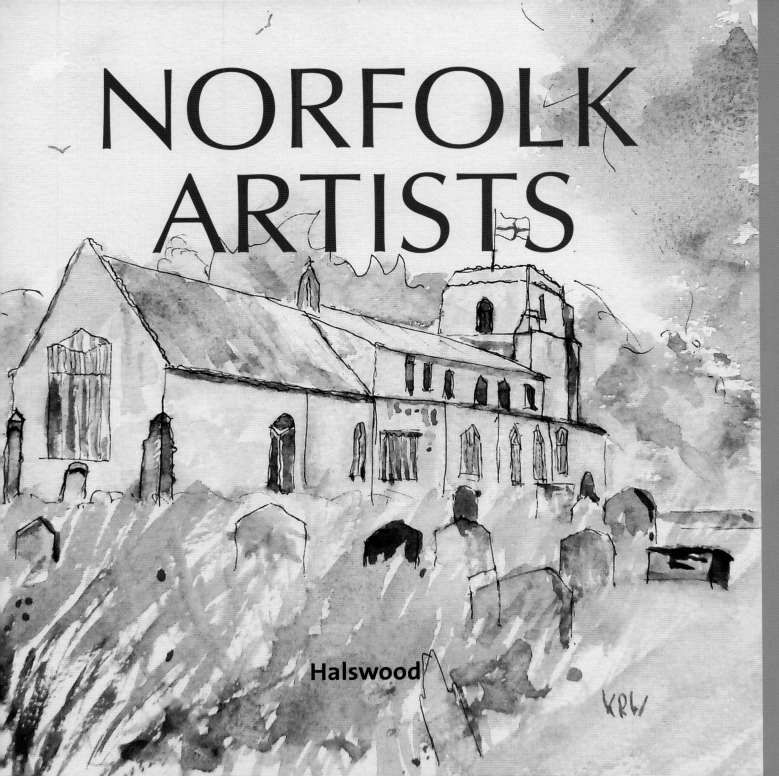

# NORFOLK ARTISTS

Halswood

Published by Halswood Stationers

British Library Cataloguing-in-Publication Data
A CIP record for this title is available
from the British Library

ISBN 978 0 85717 031 6

HALSWOOD STATIONERS
Halsgrove House,
Ryelands Industrial Estate,
Bagley Road, Wellington, Somerset TA21 9PZ
Tel: 01823 653777   Fax: 01823 216796
email: sales@halsgrove.com

Part of the Halsgrove group of companies
Information on all Halsgrove titles is available
at: www.halsgrove.com

Printed and bound in China by
Toppan Leefung Printing Ltd (0)

*Front cover:* 'Can We Go Soon?', watercolour.
**Andrew Dibben**

*Back cover: Night Flight, Stiffkey Marsh,* watercolour.
**Simon Trinder**

*Title page: St Andrews, Holt,* watercolour
**Kieron Williamson**

*Overleaf: Cromer Beach* (detail), watercolour
**Felix Bernasconi**

*Robert and Honey,* oil.
**Eddie Goodridge**

# YOUR ADDRESS BOOK

For centuries artists have found inspiration in the Norfolk landscape. The legacy of the great John Crome and John Sell Cotman has passed seamlessly through the centuries down to Munnings, Seago, and now to their modern contemporaries.

The artists whose work appears in this book are part of this long tradition. Their images have been selected to portray something of the varied range of contemporary work being created in Norfolk today. Each in their own distinctive way, captures the essence of the county. The diversity of styles included here is deliberate, as is the variety of the media in which each artist has chosen to work; traditional watercolours and oils vying with acrylics and mixed media works.

The handful of artists whose work is selected are among literally hundreds of present-day painters and photographers who are inspired to capture the elusive qualities of light, atmosphere and character that make Norfolk so special. They have been chosen as they are among the best known in the county and most have their homes and studios here. Information about each artist can be found at the end of this book. What these artists also have in common is their link with the Picturecraft Gallery in Holt whose innovative approach to promoting the best in regional art has put them at the forefront of commercial galleries for almost four decades.

Address books tend to be well used and have a long life. Along with important contact details, they keep track of the user's friends and acquaintances, tracing their lives over time and from place to place. And, if properly attended to, an address book eventually becomes something of a journal in itself, and an essential part of the household management.

Whether you have bought this book for your own use, or receive it as a gift, we hope this *Norfolk Artists Address Book,* with its superb pictorial reminders of Norfolk, provides years of pleasure.

# USEFUL ADDRESSES AND TELEPHONE NUMBERS

# A

'Can We Go Soon?', watercolour.
**Andrew Dibben**

# A

*Winter Barn Owl,* watercolour.
**Simon Trinder**

# B

*The Potato Planters*, oil.
**Eddie Goodridge**

# B

B

# B

*Impressionist Market, Norwich*, pastel.
**John Patchett**

C

*Wells Quay*, acrylic.
**June Burrows**

# C

C

# C

*Summer Reed Beds*, oil.
**Stewart Lees**

# D

*Winter scene,* pastel.
**Kieron Williamson**

# D

# D

# D

*Magical Morston*, oil.
**Brian Ryder**

E

*Winter Oaks by the Wensum*, pastel.
**Tony Garner**

E

E

# E

*Evening Flight,* oil.
**Ian Levene**

# F

*The End of the Line*, photograph.
**Bernard Dawson**

# F

F

# F

Cromer Lighthouse

G

*Cromer Lighthouse*, mixed media.
**Felix Bernasconi**

# G

G

# G

*This Must be the Place, Holt*, pastel.
**John Patchett**

Patchett

# H

Retired, photograph.
**Bernard Dawson**

# H

# H

# H

*Children Fishing,* watercolour.
**June Crawshaw**

*Toadstools*, watercolour.
**Kimberley Walker**

I

*Winter Silence at Wells*, oil.
**Stewart Lees**

J

*Incoming Tide*, acrylic.
**Trish Piggin**

# J

*Sunset Reflections, Cromer*, oil.
**Brian Ryder**

# K

*Bowthorpe, near Norwich,* watercolour.
**Felix Bernasconi**

L

L

*Across the Lake, Blicking*, oil
**Ian Levene**

L

L

# L

*Poppyfield*, pastel.
**John Patchett**

June Crawshaw

*Running Pheasant*, watercolour
**June Crawshaw**

# M

# M

# M

_Poppies,_ watercolour.
**Kimberley Walker**

*Out of the Woods, Stody Estate*, watercolour.
**Simon Trinder**

# N

*Breakers at Sheringham,* oil.
**Karen Rowlands**

O

O

*Dying Embers,* pastel.
**Tony Garner**

O

*Cley-next-the-Sea*, oil.
**Donald Belsom**

*On the Broads, at Hickling*, oil.
**Alwyn Crawshaw**

# PQ

*Stormy Seas at Walcott*, acrylic.
**Trish Piggin**

*Blakeney*, oil.
**Donald Belsom**

# R

*Norfolk Village Church*, watercolour.
**Felix Bernasconi**

# S

S

# S

*Keswick Mill,* watercolour.
**Ian Levene**

KESWICK MILL · NORFOLK

*Norfolk Pastoral,* oil.
**Ian Levene**

T

*Night Flight, Stiffkey Marsh*, watercolour.
**Simon Trinder**

*Broadland Solitude*, pastel.
**Tony Garner**

# UV

*Martini Time, Tombland*, pastel.
**John Patchett**

*Mill on the Marshes*, oil.
**Alwyn Crawshaw**

# W

*Hand in Hand*, oil.
**Caroline Richmond**

_Cutting the Field, Jack Bramley 1918_, oil.
**Eddie Goodridge**

# THE ARTISTS

The award winning PICTURECRAFT GALLERY is one of East Anglia's finest exhibition centres. Its unique 'non-commission' display system attracts some of the UK's finest professional and semi-professional artists, among them the artists features in this book. A four-weekly change of exhibits ensures a varied exhibition programme catering for all tastes, and a warm friendly welcome is extended to all visitors. Picturecraft Gallery is also renown for staging up to seven major exhibitions and/or society shows during each year. For more information visit www.picturecraftgallery.com

DONALD BELSOM 1931–2008, spent his working life as an architect, and retirement led to a home in Norfolk. Inspired by the likes of Roland Hilder and members of the Wapping Group, he spent many hours painting in oil, acrylic and watercolour. His portrayal of a winding country lane or the grandeur of Cley Mill against a stormy sky typified the quality, draftsmanship and technique of this wonderful painter.

FELIX BERNASCONI ARCA (1911–2001) dedicated much of his long life to capturing in paint the scenery of his beloved Norfolk. Trained at the Royal Academy under the eye of three 'Greats' of British art, Bawden, Ravilious and Nash, and after distinguished war service, Felix joined Jarrolds in Norwich as head of their design studio. From the 1940s onwards he spent weekends and holidays creating hundreds of paintings and sketches of rural Norfolk.

JUNE BURROWS has spent much of her life travelling and painting, finally settling in Norfolk in 1997. June works mainly in watercolour and acrylic, painting landscapes, flowers and still life as her favoured subject matter. June owned a studio and gallery in both Cyprus and Scotland.

ALWYN CRAWSHAW has exhibited at the Royal Society of British Artists in London, and with his wife June at galleries in the UK and abroad. Alwyn is a fellow of the Royal Society of Arts, a member of the British Watercolour Society, president of the National Acrylic Painters Association and an honorary member of the United Society of Artists. He is also a member of the Society of Equestrian Artists. www.alwyncrawshaw.co.uk

JUNE CRAWSHAW was born in Woking, Surrey in 1936. She married Alwyn Crawshaw in 1957, and they now both living in Norfolk. June paints in watercolour, acrylic and oil. A member of the Society of Women

Artists, British Watercolour Society and National Acrylic Painters Association, in 2000 she was made an Honorary member of the United Society of Artists. She is listed in the current edition of 'Who's Who in Art'. www.alwyncrawshaw.co.uk

BERNARD DAWSON has been a photographer for nearly 50 years. Since moving to Norfolk, 15 years ago, Bernard has concentrated on local wildlife, especially insects, but he does continue to look for those unusual angles that show the Norfolk landscape from a slightly different perspective. Bernard provided the photography for the majority of the images in this publication.

One of Norfolk's best-known artists, ANDREW DIBBEN has had his reputation for watercolours of the highest quality enhanced by the publication of two superb books of his paintings. Constantly challenging his own view of the visual features of Norfolk that he finds important, Andrew has recently been finding a new source of inspiration in some of the isolated buildings and other structures of the coastline. www.andrewdibben.com

TONY GARNER is recognised as one of East Anglia's finest painters and tutors in pastel. His paintings reveal the dramatic effect when light becomes the master of the landscape. The Norfolk landscape has provided him with a never-ending source of inspiration. www.artistsafloat.co.uk

STEWART LEES studied at Twickenham School of Art and Design and was taught by the maverick painter Stan Smith. Pursuing a career as a freelance Illustrator and Designer Stewart established a Design consultancy in 1985. Later Stewart moved his family to deepest, rural France to be a painter. He now resides and paints in Hunstanton, Norfolk. www.stewartlees.co.uk

IAN LEVENE began painting and drawing at an early age, encouraged by his father, a commercial artist, who gave him his first lessons in art. Ian now paints still life, portraits and landscapes in oils and watercolour. He has also produced artwork for greetings cards and book illustrations.

Professional artist, JOHN PATCHETT is well known for his fresh, vibrant pastel paintings. He firmly believes that it is necessary to paint, as much as possible, in 'plein air', resulting in his work having an immediacy and a strong sense of light and warmth. www.john-patchett.co.uk

TRISH PIGGIN studied art at Derbyshire College and has been painting professionally for a number of years. Successfully running her own gallery she specialised in painting cats, dogs and British wildlife. Since a return to Norfolk Trish has successfully been selling mixed media art works on box canvas using mainly acrylic to capture local sea scenes in a modern way.

CAROLINE RICHMOND has been captivated by North Norfolk's magical shoreline, the enormity of it's skies and intensity of pure light. Her evocative and dramatic portrayal of Norfolk's big skies and golden beaches are complimented by the subtle addition of a lone person walking the dog or a happy couple walking hand in hand along the shoreline. www.carolinerichmond.co.uk

KAREN ROWLANDS studied art at Ravensbourne College of Art & Design and Loughborough College of Art & Design. Working mainly in oil she paints the Norfolk landscape, in particular local wildlife and local people. www.karenrowlands.co.uk

Following a successful career in architecture, BRIAN RYDER made the decision to become a professional artist in 1993. Demand for his landscape paintings has brought him considerable recognition and he now paints in North Norfolk and runs international annual art tuition courses. He is a Provisional Member of the Royal Oil Institute. www.brianryder.org

SIMON TRINDER is a self-taught artist and has painted professionally for fifteen years. He has always concentrated on wildlife and landscapes, with an emphasis on wildfowl and wild places. www.simontrinder.com

KIMBERLEY WALKER was born in Norfolk and had an early career as a scientist. After several years as a botanical illustrator at the University of Missouri, Columbia, U.S.A., and a medical illustrator at Addenbrookes Hospital, Cambridge, Kimberley returned to Norfolk where she is currently building a full-time career from her lifelong passion to paint in watercolour.

KIERON WILLIAMSON has fast become one of the most sought after artists in the world. His rise to fame at the age of six resulted in international media coverage and sales to all four corners of the globe. Now at the tender age of seven and working in oil, watercolour and pastel, Kieron Williamson literally has the art world at his feet.